HOW I REVERSED HEART DISEASE

A Pilot's Story

John Belluardo

PAGE PUBLISHING, INC.
New York, NY

First originally published by Page Publishing, Inc. 2015

ISBN 978-1-63417-512-8 (pbk)
ISBN 978-1-63417-513-5 (digital)

Printed in the United States of America

ACKNOWLEDGMENT

A FEW THANKS ARE IN ORDER:

1. Barbara, my wife of fifty years, for supporting me in our quest to good health. Without her cooking skill, none of this could have been achieved. She also deserves a medal for putting up with me all these years!

2. Dr. Gosta Pettersson of the Cleveland Clinic. Without his skilled hands, I would not be here to tell this story.

3. The family of my donor heart valve. They literally gave me the gift of life.

4. Both Dr. Esselstyn and Dr. Campbell. Their lifelong research exposed the truth about diet and disease.

5. The angiogenesis animal researchers. They provided me with the animal model to follow.

6. Emerson Stewart and Joe Smith. Their patience and perseverance taught me the skills necessary to be a "real" pilot and achieve a lifelong dream.

7. The FAA. As much as I hate government bureaucracy, they forced me to fight and prove I could reverse heart disease.

8. John Lane. He required me to spin my Luscombe on my first check ride to earn my pilot certificate. When he was well into his eighties, he was my role model to achieve my dream.

Me, Barbara, Kay, and 83-year old Jerry finishing
The Air Force One-Half Marathon 2013

My *Young Eagles* our future *Real Pilots*

Found below are the YouTube links to the presentation made to the Academy of Surgical Research at their annual meeting held at Clearwater Beach, Florida, on September 28, 2013.

The presentation is in three parts for a total of approximately forty minutes.

Part 1: https://www.youtube.com/watch?v=cQ4dBda47H4/
Part 2: https://www.youtube.com/watch?v=Sj57fEPAtOs/
Part3: https://www.youtube.com/watch?v=FRBHLHtUx38/

HOW I REVERSED HEART DISEASE A PILOTS STORY

You are about to join me on a journey of learning lasting twenty years. We will learn both how to reverse heart disease and how to fly a *real* airplane. Hopefully, there are lessons here for both the medical and aviation communities as well as the general populace. This quote from my favorite statesman of the twentieth century is most appropriate in describing this story. "Never, never, never give up, " –Sir Winston Churchill.

I must preface the story by stating right here up front that I have no medical background and gathered all this information by doing my own research, having no preconceived notions from the medical community. As the story progresses, you will see how I took charge of my own health care and gradually unlearned all the myths we have been taught since childhood.

My story begins in 1993 being completely ignorant of heart disease. I was a partner in a successful computer hardware and software company. Much of my time was spent on the road living out of a suitcase and eating a very unhealthy diet. A typical week in Chicago would include eating at a different steak house every night. My favorite steak house was Gene & Georgetti's of Al Capone fame.

Fortunately for me, my loving wife, Barbara, encouraged me to start participating in her aerobic classes at our community recreation center. It soon became apparent that I was having difficulty keeping up with the strenuous portions of the class. I was experiencing shortness of breath as well as chest pain with exertion. Jennifer, our young aerobics instructor, was taking an evening heart rehab course and insisted that I see a doctor. With both Barbara and Jennifer ganging up on me, I finally made an appointment with our family physician who, after examining me, insisted that I see his cardiologist before he left for vacation. The cardiologist immediately scheduled me for a heart catheterization that revealed five of my heart arteries 90 percent to 95 percent blocked. In his words, "I was a heart attack waiting to happen." He scheduled me with an experienced local heart surgeon for immediate bypass surgery.

I left the hospital with five coronary bypasses on my heart. My blood work had revealed a total cholesterol reading in excess of 300 ml/dl. My cardiologist started me on a high dose of statins and advised me to change my diet.

While recovering at home, I had a lot to think about and decided a major lifestyle change was in order. I started attending a cardio rehab class at a local hospital and also returned to our aerobics class. Working on both aerobic and strength training activities, I was determined to restore my body to a healthy state. I adapted the dietary recommendations of the American Heart Association and gave up red meat entirely along with fried food. I thought I was now eating *healthy* and continued to consume both chicken and fish and used *good* olive oil to replace butter, trans fats, and saturated fats.

Here I was in my early fifties trying to restore myself to good health. My son had become a distance runner and encouraged me to join our local running club and to start running. I took the challenge and started running local five-kilometer races and trained on a regular basis. Gradually increasing my distance, I worked my way up to my first marathon, completing the Columbus Marathon on November 9, 1997, with a finish time of 4:51:53. I still have my bib #2252. This was a *mission accomplished* at restoring myself to beyond good health and achieving my goal of becoming an athlete.

My first nuclear stress test months following the surgery revealed excellent exercise tolerance and no heart ischemia. As we will see later in this story, heart ischemia or lack of blood flow and oxygen to the heart muscle will become a major driving quest for my research.

MORE HEART DISEASE!

DURING A ROUTINE PHYSICAL WITH OUR FAMILY physician, I was startled when my doctor said, "John, I hear a strange sound coming from your heart." He then scheduled me for an echocardiogram at our local hospital. When the results came back, I was informed that I had aortic stenosis. At this point, I returned to my cardiologist who had been giving me yearly treadmill stress tests and never indicated any problems. After going through open-heart surgery with five bypass grafts added to my heart, years of exams, and repeated stress tests, no one had ever bothered to take an echocardiogram of my heart! This became a turning point for me to take complete charge of my own health care. I immediately fired my cardiologist and demanded all my records. My first task was to find a new cardiologist. I had been working out at a local gym owned by an Olympic weight lifting champion who had also undergone open-heart surgery. Larry referred me to his cardiologist who accepted me and all my records. It was now time to start my *homework*. I decided I needed to learn everything there is to know about heart valves, the procedures to replace them, and who the best heart surgeons in the country were.

What better way to learn about cardiology than by taking cardiology courses online. It was very soon that I discovered Medscape and registered with the state of Ohio as a cardiologist. This gave me access to their CME courses providing Continuing Medical Education. These are the courses most doctors should be taking to maintain knowledge of their specialty. I studied all the topics related to my heart issues, even taking the tests and gathering CME point credits in my state account. Next, I found a worldwide forum of heart surgeons trading stories and comparing procedures and outcomes. I still monitor the forum to this day. I learned what worked and what didn't work as well as assimilating their worldwide knowledge of heart valves. When the time came to replace my heart valve, I was determined to make the choice mine based on my research and their experience. I would not base my decision on information provided by the pharmaceutical industry or the manufacturers of heart valves. As fate would have it, I ended up with about five years before the time came. On my journey of learning, I would discover that I was born with a bicuspid aortic valve having only two leaves instead of the normal three. The medical literature states that a bicuspid valve will calcify and wear out in the fourth to fifth decade of life. I was approaching age sixty and still running with aortic stenosis against the advice of my cardiologist. My heart had developed a hyperdynamic beat (a long, slow beat) to allow the same volume of blood to pass through a much smaller opening. I was distance running with a heartbeat of about ninety beats per minute. Before the advent of heart valve surgery, the stress on the left ventricle (the main pumping chamber of the heart) would cause the muscle to grow until it lost the ability to contract, resulting in eventual heart failure and death.

Knowing I would be facing a second heart surgery, I decided it was time for someone else to cope with the stress of running a business and *living out of a suitcase*. We sold our computer hardware and software company to a competitor. Interestingly, the deal closed on September 10, 2001, the day before 9/11. Had it been a day later, I doubt the deal would have closed.

I was now free to devote full time to my health and research. I had narrowed my search for a replacement aortic heart valve to two types. An individual's choice of valve type is a very personal one involving many factors: age, lifestyle, hemodynamics, and durability just to name a few. The two major categories are mechanical and tissue. I had eliminated the mechanical choice because of my age and the requirement of lifelong anticoagulation therapy. The drugs would not be compatible with my active lifestyle. The most common blood thinner at the time (Coumadin) was the active ingredient in rat poison, causing the rat to bleed to death. I narrowed my search down to either a Carpentier-Edwards pericardial valve (man made from the lining or pericardium of a cow's heart) or a homograft (human-donor cadaver valve).

I used some very interesting criteria to narrow down my choice of surgeons to three. While studying heart valve surgeries, I discovered the Ross procedure. It involves a double-valve transplant by removing the patient's pulmonary valve and moving it to the aortic position and then implanting a homograft valve in the pulmonary position. If a surgeon could perform hundreds of these successfully, he should be able to do a single-valve surgery *with one hand tied behind his back*. I was too old for a Ross procedure, but I wanted a surgeon with enough skill and with much experience doing difficult valve surgeries. The first surgeon I found was located at the Cleveland Clinic. The second was located at Mount Sinai Hospital in New York City. The third was located in Oklahoma City.

THE TIME FINALLY ARRIVES

BEING BORN IN BROOKLYN AND GROWING UP in New York, I have always wanted to run the New York City Marathon. We moved to Dayton Ohio in 1977, and I started my business there in 1981. I had applied to run the NYC Marathon for a number of years but hadn't been accepted since they only accept about thirty thousand applicants out of the seventy or eighty thousand entries they receive. As luck would have it, they finally accepted my entry in 2002 for New York City Marathon scheduled for November 2, 2003. Now, I had a tough decision to make. My last echocardiogram had indicated that my aortic valve was only opening about 0.6 cm². compared to a normal valve that opens somewhere between 3 to 4 cm². My left ventricle was starting to enlarge, and the pressure gradient across the valve was approaching 60 mm Hg The normal range is less than 5 mm Hg. Jack, my best friend from grade school through high school, had also been accepted and wanted to run with me. I threw caution to the wind and decided to give it a try.

Luckily for us, that 2nd day of November was a cool and sunny one with light winds. The race started on Staten Island and finished in Central Park, traversing the five boroughs of New York City. We had to cross a number of bridges including The Verrazano Narrows Bridge with a spectacular view of New York Harbor. As we approached the Queensboro Bridge (the 59th Street bridge to New Yorkers), I could only walk uphill and barely break a jog at the middle of the span, then do a slow run down to Manhattan. The entire race was a real struggle, but I made sure I was well hydrated. (My cardiologist always warned me that if I insisted on running with aortic stenosis, dehydration would cause me to keel over and die.) We were able to finish with the encouragement of one million spectators along the entire route, cheering us on with my shirt that read "I'm running on 5 bypasses & a bad valve."

DIVINE INTERVENTION

A FEW WEEKS FOLLOWING THE NEW YORK City Marathon, I had become symptomatic and was scheduled for a visit with my cardiologist. After listening to my heart, he decided I needed a heart catheterization. So here I am, shortly after running a marathon, up on a cath table at Miami Valley Hospital. We are both observing the display screen as Tom ran the cath probe from my femoral artery (the main artery that feeds blood to the leg) up into my heart and through my aortic valve, with both of us looking at the live image. I'll never forget his comment, "John, that valve needs to be replaced now! Not only is it stenotic, but also regurgitating now (leaking badly). You need to stay here and have one of our surgeons replace it." At this point in our conversation, I finally told Tom I had just completed the New York City Marathon. He said, "That is impossible. You should be dead." He convinced me that the valve had to be replaced right away. My reply took him aback when I said, "As you know, Tom, I have been studying heart valves now for five years. If I stay here in the Miami Valley Hospital, your surgeon will fit me with a St. Jude mechanical valve, and I will be living on rat poison the rest of my life." With that said, he completed the cath, doing a meticulous job knowing his images would be going to another hospital.

This is where divine intervention came into play. I was wheeled in to the recovery room where I had to lie still for a few hours with a compress on my groin. This time was required to allow my femoral artery to seal up and prevent me from bleeding out. At this point, I picked up the phone and dialed the Cleveland Clinic, asking for Dr. Gosta Pettersson. What are the odds of dialing a major hospital and having one of their top surgeons answer the phone? He answered the phone! I told him my story and the two valve types I had chosen. He asked me to stay right where I was, have some additional tests done, and have all the results sent to him at the Cleveland Clinic. He then informed me that he would operate on me the following week!

Three days later, we were at the Cleveland Clinic in a meeting with both Dr. Pettersson and his cardiologist, reviewing all my test results and medical history. Dr. Pettersson agreed with my choice of valves and suggested that since I am a runner, I would get better hemodynamics from a human donor homograft valve. There is a downside to many homograft surgeries in that the root of the valve has a tendency to dilate, causing the valve to leak and fail prematurely. With that being said, he suggested that he could obtain a section of a donor's aorta, including the intact valve from the tissue bank. I still live with his warning today. "If you should ever become a redo, you must find a very skilled surgeon to perform a difficult redo surgery." We decided to go with his suggestion, and I was scheduled for surgery the following morning.

Needless to say, I was a bit nervous in the morning and decided to run the few blocks from the hotel to the hospital with both Barbara and my son, Keith, in chase yelling at me. I considered myself to be in excellent shape and was determined to be the healthiest patient they had ever operated on. I survived the surgery and received a new aortic valve and two more bypass grafts. The only downside suffered was a half-collapsed lung on my left side. My left arm's radial artery had been removed and spliced to my heart along with my right mammary artery.

I now possessed another person's aorta and valve along with a total of seven vein and artery graft bypasses on my heart! I was close to becoming the *bionic man*.

It was Christmas week of 2003, and I had received the perfect Christmas present, "The gift of life."

I was determined to return to running and set a goal of running the next Air Force Marathon held the following September. Dr. Pettersson entered the intensive care room to remove the drain tubes from my chest. I informed him of my intention to start training for the Marathon. He explained to me that the echocardiogram he had taken of the new valve showed a normal pressure gradient of less than 5 mm Hg. I asked him if I would incur any damage to my new heart *plumbing* should I exert my heart right then. He assured me that all the internal surgery had healed. I asked, "Is there a treadmill nearby?" He replied there was one down the hall. I climbed out of bed, went down the hall to a nearby room containing the treadmill, and tried to run. My collapsed lung didn't allow me to go very fast. I was having trouble breathing and returned to my room after a brief attempt at running. I thought I had run to the surgery and decided I could run out of the surgery as well!

I was discharged from the Cleveland Clinic on Christmas day. My son, Keith, drove Barbara and me out of a Cleveland snowstorm to our home in Dayton.

I was now a veteran of two heart surgeries and skipped the rehab classes and instead worked on strength training at the gym along with aerobic classes at our recreation center. I enjoyed being the only guy in a class of about thirty women. I tried to run but was having trouble with my breathing. During the second week following surgery, while doing aerobics in our class, I started to cough violently. My breathing came back to normal! My left lung had apparently opened fully. Now, I resumed my marathon training runs, gradually adding distance at about 10 percent a week. I waited about five weeks to strengthen my chest with push-ups. It took about six months before I could do them without chest pain. As the weeks grew into months, I was running 5K and 10K races on a regular basis.

At midyear, I decided it was time to give a half marathon a try and entered the Parkersburg, West Virginia, one-half marathon. This would serve as a training run for my upcoming marathon. It is a beautiful hilly course well supported by some wonderful people, included was a really nice pasta dinner the night before the race. I completed the race on a warm, sunny summer day and was presented with a beautiful stone finisher's medal. I drove back to Dayton and showed the stone medal to Barbara. Then I was struck with a thought. I had completed that race with a heart valve and a section of my aorta donated by an anonymous human donor. There was a family out there somewhere that had lost a loved one and given life to others not knowing the good they had done. I felt I had to find a way to thank them. I pulled my Cleveland Clinic records and found a serial number had been assigned by LifeNet for tracking purposes. They were located in Virginia Beach. I sat down and drafted a thank you letter to the family that had donated my heart valve and attached the beautiful stone finisher's medal to the letter. I placed the letter and medal inside a cover letter addressed to LifeNet. I asked them to please forward my letter to the family that had donated my heart valve. It was a long shot, but I had to try.

One day, a couple of months later, I went out to our mailbox and found a letter from LifeNet. Opening it, I found another letter written by the mother of my donor. As I read it, I started to cry like a baby. She thanked me for the medal and went on to described her twenty-nine-year-old son who had been killed in a car wreck. She told me about the kind of person he was and his likes and dislikes. To this day, my running shirt has a print on the front and back, saying, "I'm Running on a Donated Heart valve." I feel it is so important that the public be aware of organ donation. They are literally giving *the gift of life* when donating organs from a loved one.

MISSION ACCOMPLISHED

ON SEPTEMBER 19, 2004, I COMPLETED THE Air Force Marathon and received another beautiful medal. This was a large bronze medal with the image of the F-117A Nighthawk. It was time to say thank you again. I informed Barbara that we would be driving to Cleveland. When we arrived at the Cleveland Clinic, we looked for Dr. Pettersson and found him in his office. I presented him with the medal, placing it around his neck. He was more deserving of the medal than I was! He had literally given me a new lease on life. The valve he placed in me is still working fine after eleven years with no leaks. My last echo cardiogram showed no calcium on the implant, and it is actually working better than my three native valves! To this day, I treasure the picture of me standing next to Dr. Pettersson, wearing the medal *he* earned with the artistry of his hands.

My first nuclear stress test six months following the surgery came up clean, showing no ischemia and normal profusion to my heart muscle. I continued to strength train and run. As the years passed, I weaned my running from pavement and limited all my running to trails except for the Air Force one-half marathons that I continue to run every year to this day. It has become an annual event for us. We have learned to cross train by adding distance biking and the elliptical trainer to our daily exercise routines.

It is important to note at this point in my story that exercise alone cannot prevent heart disease as we are soon to discover.

A BOYHOOD DREAM: "I WANT TO FLY"

WE FAST-FORWARD NOW TO 2006. I HAD always wanted to fly. I have fond memories of building model airplanes as a child, flying them, and wanting to learn how to fly. Like many of us, we put our dreams on hold as life's priorities take precedence over our lives. At this stage of life, Barbara and I had become almost full-time caregivers for our aging moms. Both were suffering from progressive dementia, requiring more of our attention and time. I needed a challenging activity that would alter my routine. Andy, one of our friends, was heavily involved in antique aviation and suggested that I take some traditional Stick & Rudder flying lessons in a *tail dragger* trainer. At age sixty-three, I would finally realize my dream of flying. He suggested that I take my lessons at a *grass roots* family run airport just south of Dayton. The grass strip located in Waynesville, Ohio, is considered one of the finest tail wheel schools in the country attracting students from other states. I have vivid memories of my first few lessons in their 1946 Aeronca Champ and Piper Cub. Just taxiing on the grass was a real challenge. You must steer the tail wheel with your feet while sitting in the backseat unable to see over the nose and perform S-turns from side to side to see forward. The plane's center of gravity is behind the main landing gear. The back literally wants to go to the front. For the reader without any flying experience, I would liken it to pushing a shopping cart from the wrong end or driving your car down the interstate in reverse, steering from the back. For this reason, I refer to tail wheel aircraft as *real airplanes* and nose wheel airplanes as being equipped with *training wheels*. When landing a nose wheel airplane in a crosswind, the pilot can approach the runway in a *crab*, and as the aircraft touches down, it will straighten itself out since the center of gravity is forward of the main landing gear. If the pilot of a *tail dragger* tried a crab touchdown in a crosswind, at best, the plane would do a ground loop. At worst, it would end up on its back.

You might ask what all these has to do with heart disease. The FAA (Federal Aviation Administration) requires a pilot to pass a physical exam and obtain a medical certificate. Just passing a physical exam is not enough. Should the applicant have any history of disease like heart disease, then a whole battery of tests must be taken and passed. I could master the art of flight with a certified flight instructor in the aircraft with me, but at some point, I would have to obtain a medical certificate. At this point in my story, I had survived two open-heart surgeries, followed all the recommendations of the medical community, and I was running marathons. *I am in excellent physical condition and can pass any test thrown at me.* And I was about to discover I was wrong. Andy gave me the name of his AME (Airman Medical Examiner), and I took my first physical exam, passing it without any problem. The AME could not issue me a medical certificate following the physical exam because I had listed my history of heart disease on the form, requiring him to forward it to the FAA in Oklahoma City for approval. The FAA Office of Aerospace Medicine reviewed my application and requested a nuclear stress test. My cardiologist performed the test and sent the results to the FAA. I continued my flying lessons while waiting many months for a reply. Then the reply finally arrived. They wrote that I did not meet their required medical standards because of both the coronary bypasses on my heart as well as having a replaced heart valve. They considered me for what they call *a special issue medical cer-*

tificate. Now here is the show stopper that launched my next phase of research. "We have been unable to find you qualified due to objective evidence of ischemia on your exercise stress testing." As I would soon find out, I had a daunting task ahead of me trying to convince the FAA that they were wrong. A pilot friend had a physical exam with the same AME and heard the comment "the FAA will never pass John with his heart history." As we will see, I had my work cut out.

ISCHEMIA

Ischemia as defined by the dictionary: "A decrease in the blood supply to a bodily organ, tissue, or part caused by constriction or obstruction of the blood vessels." I immediately started a search for *reverse ischemia* and found Dr. Caldwell B. Esselstyn and his then newly released book *Prevent and Reverse Heart Disease*. I read his book from cover to cover and also read a book he recommended, *The China Study* by Dr. Colin Campbell. Both books address the *cause* of heart and other diseases. Now I had confirmation that the mainstream medical community was being driven by the pharmaceutical industry and surgeries that addressed the symptoms of heart disease and not the cause. The most common heart surgery performed to this day is coronary bypass surgery. The most common procedure performed by cardiologists is the placement of stents in blocked arteries. Both procedures address symptoms and have nothing to do with the cause of heart disease. Over the years, I have become friends with Dr. Esselstyn; and we will see later in my story how my research on angiogenesis was influenced by a comment he made while Barbara and I were visiting him and his wife, Ann, at their home in Cleveland. One of Dr. Esselstyne's favorite sayings is "diet trumps everything." I will add that it also trumps genetics. All of my first cousins died of heart disease in their early sixties! There is no magic pill to replace diet. I hate to use the word diet since there are so many fad diets driven by monetary gain. Dr. Esselstyne's book is an *easy* read having the second half filled with recipes. Dr. Campbell's book describes his lifelong research on diet and disease. *The China Study* analyzed the diets, blood lipids, and diseases of rural China over a twenty-year period. The movie *Forks over Knives* featuring both doctors is now available on video. As an interesting side note, both doctors grew up on dairy farms.

In April 2007, Barbara and I started eating plant-based whole food with no added oil and no dairy products. I was determined to reverse my heart disease and prove to the FAA I could eliminate the ischemia they had uncovered in the left ventricle of my heart. Within weeks, I felt a difference in my running, endurance, and overall health. My next blood test showed a dramatic decrease in my blood lipids. My total cholesterol dropped to 96 mg/dL. My LDL dropped to 31 mg/dL.

Based on my research of others suffering from arterial heart disease, those patients who kept a strict adherence to the diet would see some significant reversal of the buildup of plaque in their arteries after about three years. I would have to wait before I could prove this to the FAA with documented results.

With this in mind, I decided to purchase my own plane and continue my flying lessons. I had originally thought about purchasing a 1930s open-cockpit biplane. As time passed and my flying skills grew, I decided to purchase an aircraft that could carry Barbara, me, and baggage for cross-country trips to visit family and friends. The trainers I had been flying had tandem seating and very limited storage space for baggage. I wanted side by side seating and a decent-sized storage area for baggage. I narrowed my search to three affordable classic side-by-side tail draggers. The Taylorcraft, Aeronca Chief, and the Luscombe model 8. I found a Taylorcraft nearby at Warren County Airport (now renamed John Lane Memorial Airport) owned by certified flight instructor and local flying legend, John Lane, who had started the airport from a family farm. I took a few lessons with John who was the last CFI in the area to require his students to spin the aircraft in order to pass their check ride. And yes, I did spin the Taylorcraft during one of my lessons. I didn't like the obstructed view from the pilot's seat when looking to either side. The pilot's head needs to be tilted down to see below the wing root. It was also equipped with a yoke and slow to respond to control changes. Next, I found a freshly restored Aeronca Chief located at Moraine Airpark up for sale. Tim, the local CFI on the field, gave me a flying lesson in it. I found it had similar flying characteristics with the Aeronca Champ I had been taking lessons in.

Mark, a local friend at my home field, just finished restoring his 1946 Luscombe model 8A. I asked him for a ride, and he took me up. Once aloft, he let me take the controls, and it was love at first sight! First, it was a classic stick and rudder machine unlike the Taylorcraft and Chief equipped with a yoke. Second, it was monocoque (stressed skin aluminum) construction as opposed to steel tube and fabric of its contemporaries. Third, it was very responsive on the controls and fun to fly.

I started a countrywide search for a Luscombe with the features I desired. I found a few for sale within driving distance from home. After inspecting them, they either had condition issues or lacked the features I desired. I kept searching patiently the ads for about a year on an almost daily basis and finally found a new posting on Barnstormers (the premier Web site for selling things about aviation). It had all the features I was looking for, including two 12.5 gal wing tanks, inertial reel retractable shoulder harnesses, an extended baggage compartment, lightweight custom seats, a retractable tail pull, and best of all, it was nonelectric and powered by a Continental A-65. The secret to a good flying Luscombe is to keep it light with no battery, starter motor, generator, or unnecessary instrumentation. In my eyes, this was the perfect aircraft for our needs. It was located at a small private grass field (27XS Sport Flyers Airport) just north of Brookshire, Texas. I immediately contacted Eric, the owner, and agreed to a deposit with purchase pending inspection. As a student pilot, I would have to buy two commercial tickets to Houston for myself and Emerson, my primary instructor. The description in the ad sounded good, but I did not want to waste our time and money and find a piece of junk not worth the trip. After all, I was looking to purchase an aircraft nearly seventy years old. Unfortunately, Luscombes have unfairly been given a reputation for being very difficult to land, especially in a crosswind and described by some pilots as *squirrely*. I have found the Luscombe to be one of the most responsive aircraft I have ever flown and quick on the controls when needed in gusty crosswind conditions. In my opinion, the reputation is due to *squirrely* pilots! Almost all old tail draggers have been ground looped, flipped over, or wrecked once or multiple times in their history. I followed my instinct and ordered up a history of both ownership and repair available via CD from the FAA at a cost of $10. Next, I located an A&P (Airframe & Power plant mechanic) who held an AI (Inspection Authorization). I called airports within driving distance of Brookshire, looking for an A&P with Luscombe experience. I was given the name of one who worked at a neighboring field. I contacted him, and he agreed to do a prebuy inspection for me. It was the best $100 investment I have ever made! He spent a day looking it over and reported back that it was definitely worth my trip. He also e-mailed me a detailed inspection report. In the interim, the FAA CD arrived with ownership and repair records starting at July 22, 1946. The day N71767 Luscombe 8A serial #3194 left the factory. It should be noted that the TC #694 (CAA Type Certification) dates back to 1937. The early production Luscombes, though made with aluminum construction, were built with aluminum-ribbed wings covered in fabric. The week this Luscombe left the factory, they had switched over to all-aluminum wings. I was fascinated tracking all the previous owners and different States where it had spent time. At one point, it had been fitted with skis in the upper Midwest. The repair records indicated it had been wrecked at least three times! The last wreck in the state of Washington occurred in 1996, resulting in a major rebuilding of the airframe in the shop that had installed the harnesses and tail pull. I called them to see if they had any additional information on the rebuild. A fellow in the shop remembered the plane and told me that an old timer who had since *gone west* had been an artist with aluminum and riveting and had replaced much of the lower skins and done a meticulous job of putting it back to airworthy condition. I wish I knew his name. Because of his work, that little airplane is responsible for my love of flying and my quest to reverse heart disease!

I purchased commercial tickets for Emerson and myself. We flew to Houston on Easter weekend of April 2008. We rented a car and drove to Sport Flyers, spending that evening and all of the next day going over Lil Buster (the name painted on the nose by a previous owner) with a fine toothed comb. I was especially looking for any corrosion on the airframe and inside the wings. We found none. Indeed that old timer had replaced anything questionable, and his rivet work on the new aluminum skins looked superior to the original factory work. We uncovered one minor problem in the airframe. A flat spot on a pulley in the tail that was easily replaced. The engine was another issue. We found lots of leaked oil on the cowl that appeared to be coming from leaking pushrod tubes. We checked the engine log, and it showed that the crankshaft had been replaced a few hundred hours ago. We had completed the inspection, and I consummated the sale with the Eric.

THE TRIP HOME

WE TOOK OFF EARLY THE NEXT MORNING with three extra quarts of oil behind the seat and Emerson in the left seat. We did a low pass over the field to say good-bye to Eric and headed north toward our first gas stop on our almost 1000-mile journey to Red Stewart Field and home. Once aloft, Emerson turned the controls over to me. I practiced my pilotage (the classic method of navigating), following the red lines I had drawn on the sectional charts and spotting landmarks along our route of flight. At this point, I had never landed a Luscombe and soon learned how responsive it really is! It was not as forgiving as the Piper Cub I had learned on. I was over controlling on my first couple of landing attempts. We made three gas stops and landed at (40I) home just as it was getting dark. I had a whole new respect for the Luscombe and did a perfect landing on our home field! The 1000-mile trip had been the perfect learning experience to familiarize myself with my *new* plane.

FIRST SOLO

I WAS NOW TAKING MOST OF MY instruction from Joe Smith. We had planned to do our longest trip to date from Red Stewart Field in Waynesville to Burke Lakefront in Cleveland. I had changed the oil the night before and prepared my sectional charts for our new adventure. It was the morning of March 30, 2009. It had been ten months since flying Buster home from Houston. I had taken quite a few lessons and felt ready to *leave the nest.* Before we took off for our trip, Joe mentioned that he could smell oil and saw smoke coming from the engine. I thought I may have spilled some oil on the manifold the night before. Joe stopped me on the runway and jumped out telling me to fly around the pattern, and he would watch for smoke. I thought nothing of it and proceeded to take off, fly the pattern, and land to pick him up for our flight to Cleveland. With a big smile on his face, he said, "John, you just soloed." He had tricked me into my solo, thinking I was troubleshooting the engine! We never did make it to Cleveland and had to land in Medina, my alternate airport, in case Burke Lakefront was socked in—a common occurrence in early spring. I'll never forget that day. I broke the tail wheel spring for the second time landing in Medina. After lunch and a local temporary fix by the FBO, we flew back home. When we landed, they tore off the back of my shirt, and Joe did his first solo artwork as is the long-standing tradition.

"John Belluardo is a pilot" read the sign in front of the airport.

I was now chomping at the bit to start my adventures. I chose John Lane to give me my check ride. He had issued my student pilot certificate even though I was still fighting with the FAA over the ischemia issue. Joe prepared me by having me fly all the required maneuvers in every weather and runway condition he could throw at me. He wanted to make sure I could pass muster with the *spin master*, John Lane. In the morning of May 6, 2009, I flew Buster over to Warren County Airport (John Lane Memorial). It was a drab overcast day with light drizzle falling. John gave me my verbal test, and then we went up. I had to demonstrate my navigational skills, aerial maneuvers, and emergency landing procedures. He was quite a character. Without warning, he would pull the throttle out and shout, "Find a suitable place to make an emergency landing." I had to turn into the wind and head for a farm field that looked like it would work. I think I surprised him when I almost touched down in a field with a fence in the way when he pushed the throttle back in. Last but not least, without any warning, he grabbed the controls and threw the plane into a tailspin. Again, I think I surprised him when I kept Buster spinning and asked, "How many turns do you want?" I pulled out with plenty to spare. We landed and John issued me my pilot's certificate. I still carry that paper certificate in my wallet with John's signature on it. It means more to me than the plastic one issued by the FAA years later. I had been taught well. I owe a big thank you to Joe and Emerson who taught the *old timer* to feel like a kid again! Within days, I started taking passengers up, starting with Barb's dear friend, Rose, who always screamed every time I banked a turn. Ironically, we lost our dear friend, Rose, to a car accident last year. To this day, if anyone asks if flying a small plane is dangerous, I reply, "The most dangerous part of flying is driving to the airport."

MAJOR OVERHAUL

ALL AIRCRAFTS MUST UNDERGO AN ANNUAL INSPECTION to maintain their airworthiness. With me assisting Cub Stewart, my A&P, we took Buster apart for inspection and performed all the required maintenance of an annual inspection. I took it upon myself to stop all the oil leaks from the pushrod tubes by removing them and using a swaging tool to seal them back in place. I felt good having stopped the oil leaks. I replaced the cowl and started my run up tests to make sure no oil was leaking. After completing my run up and opening the cowl, all the leaks were gone except for a trickle of oil dripping between two cylinders. After close inspection, I discovered a crack in the engine case. After some contemplation, I resigned myself to the task at hand. As things were, this turned out to be a blessing in disguise. Upon tearing down the engine, we found both the main and rod bearings lacking their proper linings. I commented to Cubby, "But what about the replaced crankshaft in the engine logbook?" I'll never forget his response. "The only difference between an aircraft logbook and a fairy tale is that the fairy tale begins with 'once upon a time. '"

Before I proceed with this part of the story, an explanation is in order. Though I am not a certified aircraft mechanic and my formal training is in computer science and electronics, I attended a vocational high school and was trained as an auto mechanic. I have rebuilt a number of engines, including those in my antique automobiles. Two of which are powered by Lycoming engines.

I had all the tools and knowledge to overhaul my Continental A-65 engine. I had also purchased a 1944 Continental Overhaul manual and read it from cover to cover. When I approached Cubby, I said, "If I am going to fly my wife all over the country in this bird, I want to overhaul this engine myself." At that point Cubby had seen my work and tools and agreed if he could "look over my shoulder and sign off my work at each stage of restoring the engine back to 'zero time'.

We proceeded with the project under Cubby's supervision. When the time came for machine work, I specified some additional procedures for the machine shop. I had the crankshaft reground to specification and added the requirement to have the crank journals nitrided to harden and strengthen them as is the practice in building a modern engine. I also had the crankshaft, connecting rods, and pistons balanced. This would provide for a very smooth running engine. Upon completion, we did the required ground run ups, and I proceeded to circle the field for hours to start the initial break-in of the now zero-time engine. I was now completely familiar with both the airframe and engine having put the engine together with my own two hands and Cubby's calibrated torque wrench. I had also rebuilt the carburetor myself with Cubby watching, of course. It still starts on the first pull of the prop to this day.

OUR FIRST LONG
CROSS-COUNTRY FLIGHT

THAT SEPTEMBER, BARBARA AND I HAD PLANNED to visit my brother just south of Syracuse, New York, and then on to the New York City area to visit friends and hike the Appalachian trail with my boyhood friend, Jack. What better way to get flying experience than flying an antique aircraft with no electrical system to New York City?

Most nonpilots always ask me, "How can you fly into a busy place like New York City with a nonelectric aircraft?" There is an FAA rule that states that if an aircraft was originally built without an engine-driven electrical system, it is exempt from the requirement to have a transponder or any electrical instrument. A pilot can enter controlled airspace as long as he or she carries a handheld portable radio and can talk to approach control or the airport control tower. I fly under the class B airspace of LaGuardia, Kennedy, and Newark and use outlying airports like Morristown, New Jersey or Republic Field on Long Island. It is kind of fun to fly around LaGuardia and watch the *big iron* making approaches above us. When we do land at a controlled airport in the New York area and call the tower "Luscombe 71767," I usually get a response from the air traffic controller, "What are you flying?" immediately followed with, "Luscombe, your transponder must be broken. I have no signal on my scope." To which I respond, "Negative transponder. This is a nonelectric. We are flying a real airplane." We flew the Luscombe from Dayton to New York City with a stop in Chittenango, New York, and back to Dayton. While in New York, we flew at 900 ft. down the Hudson River, over both the George Washington and Verrazano bridges. We have some great pictures. We were thrilled to fly over Ellis Island where my grandfather landed in 1905 with $9 in his pocket. Barbara took a great picture as I flew directly in front of the Statue of Liberty. We also flew over my birthplace, Bay Ridge, Brooklyn.

Flying down the Hudson River over the George Washington Bridge

Flying over Ellis Island where my grandfather landed
on June 27, 1905, with $9 in his pocket

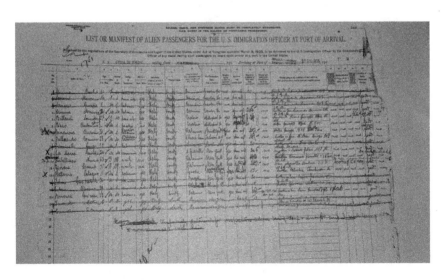

The ship's manifest showing Tommaso Belluardo arriving
at the port of New York SS "City of Turin."

Barbara and John flying in front of the Statue
of Liberty at an altitude of 900 feet

Approaching the Verrazano–Narrows Bridge
and my birthplace, Bay Ridge, Brooklyn

HOW NOT TO TAKE FLYING LESSONS

FOR A TIME, WHILE WAITING FOR RESPONSES from many requests to the FAA, I developed a new strategy. As I pointed out at the beginning of this story, Red Stewart Field is one of the most popular tail wheel schools in the country and requires students to secure appointments for lessons sometimes weeks or months in advance. With our care-giving duties taking more time, along with my exercise schedule including the gym, running, and biking, I was having trouble keeping appointments. In addition, I was still taking cardiology courses and monitoring the heart surgery forum. One of the Red Stewart Field rules restricts their planes from going up if crosswinds exceed 10 kt. I now had my own plane and would just wait until the weather turned bad and drive out to the field when most students were afraid to fly. If Joe or Emerson were not available, I would then find any pilot who possessed a certificate as a CFI (certified flight instructor). Many of the local CFIs were aerobatic pilots who performed at air shows. Most of the flight manuals recommend staying with one instructor. I was now taking lessons with many different CFIs in high winds, rain, and even snow. Every time I went up with a new guy, he would want to test me since I was *old* for learning how to fly. Typically, the new CFI would have me climb to 3,500 ft. and throw me into a spin. It finally got to the point if I encountered a CFI I had never flown with, I would climb to 3,500 ft. and ask, "Which way would you like to spin, to the left or to the right?" They taught me how to make aerobatic turns, loops, rolls, and of course, spins. Now I understood where the saying "if you can fly a Luscombe, you can fly anything" came from. By modern standards, the Luscombe model 8 is not designated as an aerobatic aircraft; but when it was designed in 1937, there was no such designation. I might add that the maneuvers I perform on occasion are benign if done correctly and put no undue stress on the airframe. That being said, I've been told many times, "John, you shouldn't be doing aerobatics in a seventy-year-old airframe."

For the reader wishing to experience aerobatics in my Luscombe, here is a link to an HD video I made by mounting a camera on my left wing. The video has a nice perspective facing forward showing, Buster's nose and propeller on the right side for a good frame of reference. It is approximately three minutes in duration and shows three loops followed by a three-turn spin then a combination of a turn and half spin directly into a loop. Note that I must dive coming out of the spin to gather enough air speed to perform the last loop. The video ends with a landing on a muddy Red Stewart Field. That is me shaking hands with Joe Smith at the end. Enjoy: https://www.youtube.com/watch?v=GERbE-6VvbY/

If we received any accumulation of snow, the grass field would close. The Stewarts would fit one of their Cubs with skis, and I could take lessons landing and taking off on snow. That following summer, I took some glider lessons and sharpened my nonpowered flight skills. Just ask Sully Sullenberger if his glider training helped him land a nonpowered airliner safely on the Hudson River.

Time for a glider lesson.

I will add one winter experience with a CFI who shall remain nameless. I showed up one blustery winter afternoon with snow flurries in the area and temperatures hovering at the freezing mark. We went up to about 2, 500 feet and headed north toward Dayton. As we approached my neighborhood, we encountered a snow squall. I was about to turn away when the CFI said, "Fly into the squall." I did as directed and within thirty seconds, the windshield was covered in white rime ice. I now had no front visibility! He calmly said, "Find your way back to the airport and land this plane." The Luscombe has side windows that open out at the bottom. I opened my window and could see straight down. I was over my home neighborhood and practically over my house. I followed the roads I use to drive to the airport and made my way back to Waynesville and landed with only vision from the open side window. Now that was one hell of a flying lesson never to be forgotten! It taught me to *never* fly at the freezing level on a day with any type of precipitation.

"IS THE DIET WORKING?"

I NEEDED TO FIND A METHOD OF getting some detailed images of my heart. I discovered that Christ Hospital in Cincinnati was planning to install a Siemens 64 slice CT scanner. At the time, this was a state-of-the-art machine that could provide the necessary information I desired. I located the Siemens salesman who was handling their account and asked him if I could volunteer as a test subject when their engineers installed the machine. I added that I had some interesting *plumbing* on my heart and would make for an ideal test subject. The hospital was also holding a training class for cardiology students in conjunction with the installation. I drove to Cincinnati and filled out all the necessary forms, signed a release, and was scheduled for the scan. I found a means of obtaining an expensive coronary CT angiogram at no cost. I was scanned about six weeks later and subsequently received both the images and a detailed report. The results startled me. Five of the grafts on my heart had occluded, yet my perfusion was normal. I contacted Dr. Esselstyn and made arrangements to meet him at one of his seminars in Cleveland. That evening, he invited Barbara and me to his home where we also met his wonderful wife, Ann. I shared both the CT images and the cardiology report with him. One of the comments he made stuck in my mind. He indicated that he had angiogram images of his patients showing reversal in their native arteries. He was concerned that I had so many bypass grafts and that once a partially blocked native artery is bypassed, the native artery closes off completely and dies. That comment haunted me as we traveled home the next morning. I was both troubled and challenged at the same time. The following day, I did a search on growing arteries. The search resulted in a process called angiogenesis.

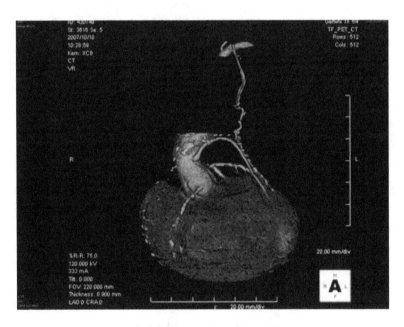

CT image of my heart

ANGIOGENESIS

THIS IS HOW WIKIPEDIA DEFINES ANGIOGENESIS: "ANGIOGENESIS is the physiological process through which new blood vessels form from pre-existing vessels. This is distinct from vasculogenesis, which is the *de novo* formation of endothelial cells from mesoderm cell precursors. The first vessels in the developing embryo form through vasculogenesis, after which angiogenesis is responsible for most, if not all, blood vessel growth during development and in disease. Angiogenesis is a normal and vital process in growth and development, as well as in wound healing and in the formation of granulation tissue. However, it is also a fundamental step in the transition of tumors from a benign state to a malignant one, leading to the use of angiogenesis inhibitors in the treatment of cancer. The essential role of angiogenesis in tumor growth was first proposed in 1971 by Judah Folkman, who described tumors as 'hot and bloody.' "

I started reading research papers on human angiogenesis and uncovered many studies primarily dealing with cancer. They were directed at inhibiting tumor growth by restricting angiogenesis.

Methods of promoting angiogenesis in the human heart involved injecting stem cells into damaged heart tissue or using lasers to make holes in the ischemic heart muscle to try and promote vascular growth. Other methods involved VEGF (vascular endothelial growth factor) and how to promote endothelial growth (the interior lining of arteries) to revasculate ischemic heart tissue. These methods all appeared to have limited promise. My quest for angiogenesis research, resulting in substantial artery growth led me to animal studies. Here I uncovered a number of studies based on nothing exotic, but the simple premise that ischemic tissue in any living creature will respond with angiogenesis when placed under stress. A number of animal models had been used, including dogs, rabbits, or rats. The animal models had healthy tissue in their legs that had been artificially made ischemic by ligating their femoral arteries (the major artery that feeds blood to the leg). Then they were typically forced to run on a treadmill for approximately two hours a session with restricted blood flow to their leg muscle. After a two-week period, an angiogram would be taken of the leg. The images would show a network of arteries had grown around the ligated femoral artery. In effect, the blockage had been bypassed via angiogenesis. Human heart disease is the product of a poor lifestyle exacerbated by poor diet and lack of exercise. This results in blockage of the coronary arteries over time. The laboratory animal subjects, on the other hand, are fed a balanced chow and have healthy endothelial cells lining their arteries and capillaries allowing them to respond to stress with angiogenesis. Could this process be duplicated in a human heart? As we will see, I believed it could, provided the endothelial cells of the test subject were in a healthy state. I searched the medical literature files and could find no such studies on humans. I could find evidence of limited collateral growth in some heart patients but no evidence of any medical research facility forcing a patient deliberately into heart ischemia to grow coronary arteries. I'm sure the liability issues would discourage any researcher from attempting such research. I did not believe it would work on a diseased human heart since their coronary arteries are lined with endothelial cells incapable of responding to stress resulting in a probable myocardial infarction.

I also uncovered much evidence of healthy athletes significantly increasing both their oxygen uptake (VO_2 max) and aerobic endurance. They repeatedly stressed their cardiovascular systems, following an intense interval exercise protocol. Many Olympic athletes have followed such protocols to dramatically improve their performance, examples dating all the way back to Jesse Owens training for the 1936 Berlin Olympics.

THE MOMENT OF TRUTH

Was I willing to put my common sense theory of reversing heart disease to the test? Barbara and I were eating plant-based whole food, and I was exercising on an almost daily basis. Were my coronary endothelial cells healthy enough to respond to the same stress the laboratory animals were subject to? All my recent nuclear stress tests had shown left ventricle heart ischemia. How could I gauge the degree of ischemia placed on my heart during intense exercise without pushing my heart into a myocardial infarction? These were tough questions, and to make matters worse, I had to find a way to do this on my own with no help from anyone. No medical professional would ever agree to be part of such a plan.

I decided I would use an elliptical trainer equipped with arms. I could increase the resistance and speed to any desired level without tearing up my joints or subjecting my body to any repetitive impact. I planned on maintaining my heart in ischemia for two-hour sessions similar to the routine used on the laboratory animals. I had a membership at an exercise facility about two miles from home. It was equipped with a whole bank of Life Fitness elliptical trainers. They were programmed to end their workout time at twenty minutes. A search of the model number on the Internet quickly revealed their programming instructions. I would avoid the gym's *busy times* and program the machine for maximum time at the start of my workout then reprogram it back to a twenty-minute duration upon completion of my workout.

ECG

Before I proceed with my story, a short explanation of ECG is in order: Electrocardiography (ECG or EKG from Greek: *kardia,* which means heart) is a transthoracic (across the thorax or chest) interpretation of the electrical activity of the heart over a period of time, as detected by electrodes attached to the surface of the skin and recorded by a device external to the body. The recording produced by this non-invasive procedure is termed an electrocardiogram (also ECG or EKG).

An ECG is used to measure the rate and regularity of heartbeats, as well as the size and position of the chambers, the presence of any damage to the heart, and the effects of drugs or devices used to regulate the heart, such as a pacemaker.

Most ECGs are performed for diagnostic or research purposes on human hearts but may also be performed on animals, usually for diagnosis of heart abnormalities or research.

How could I monitor my level of heart ischemia during exercise?

I needed a tool to monitor my heart while I drove it into ischemia. My *bag of tricks* contained an old Holter monitor I had purchased on eBay a few years ago for a couple of hundred bucks. It was an older technology and larger than the newer units and had a built-in display capable of displaying ECG in real time as well as the ability to record up to twenty-four hours of the patient's ECG. I purchased it because I was experiencing premature ventricular contractions (PVCs) following my last surgery. I was doing quite a bit of running and wanted to record my ECG over the entire duration of a race and then either display or print it. I had found some Windows-based drivers and utilities designed for this particular manufacturer's model. I integrated the utilities into an application on my laptop and was able to upload my entire ECG race history. I could then scroll through the ECG waveform, looking at where I was experiencing PVCs during a race. I had the ability to print a detailed strip of the entire race or portions of it. I used it for a number of races, trying different exertion levels at various distances to observe the effect on my ECG waveform. I finally arrived at the conclusion that my PVCs were benign and nothing to worry about. The monitor had been sitting in my *bag of tricks* for a couple of years unused. I would now resurrect it for a new use.

MORE HOMEWORK

I NEEDED TO *BONE UP* A BIT on reading ECGs. I also maintain a file of all my stress tests. I had copies of every test my cardiologist submitted to the FAA on an almost yearly basis. They contained the cardiologist's *impressions* as well as the rhythm strip of my heart at various stages in the stress test. I was being rejected by the FAA for ischemia as indicated by depression of the ST segment of my ECG and the radio isotope images showing ischemia at stress when compared to my rest images. I studied my ECG rhythm strips at the higher stages of the stress tests and familiarized myself with the waveform, paying special attention to the ST segment as it progressed below 2 cm. of the center line on the trace, indicating left ventricle ischemia. Armed with this knowledge, it was time to put my theory to practice. I now had a tool I could use to monitor my heart at various stress levels, thus allowing me to modulate the work load on my heart by increasing or decreasing the speed and resistance on the elliptical trainer and observe my heart ischemia in real time. I planned on initially following the basic protocol used on the lab animals for a two-week period, transitioning to an interval protocol of my own design based on a combination of protocols followed by athletes to improve their performance. If correct, I should see an improvement in the ST segment of my ECG somewhere in the vicinity of two weeks. I could then eliminate the Holter monitor for my workouts and return to my trusty Polar heart rate monitor watch I had purchased in 1993 after my first heart surgery. I could then follow the protocol based on my heart rate. I only needed two more items to begin: a package of fresh AA alkaline batteries and a new box of quality electrodes for the Holter leads. My research would not be very costly. After a visit to a local medical supply store for electrodes and a stop at a big box store for batteries, I was ready to go.

THE FIRST TWO-HOUR SESSION

I HAD MEMBERSHIPS AT THREE DIFFERENT EXERCISE facilities and chose the Trent Arena Fitness Center because of their large number of elliptical trainers and convenient location from my home. They also had no formal training classes, and the place would be nearly empty at off peak hours. I needed at least two hours and chose to avoid early morning and early evening when the fitness center is busy. The morning of the workout, I placed the electrodes on my chest in their appropriate locations and then snapped the color-coded lead wires in place. I also wore my wireless polar chest trap that transmitted my heart rate to the elliptical trainer for display. This would allow me to easily correlate my heart rate with the waveform on the monitor display without having to calculate heart rate based on the frequency of the QRS segment peaks in the waveform. I filled my water bottle with tap water. I was going to make sure I was well hydrated during the workout. When I arrived at the center, all the elliptical trainers were empty. I picked my favorite with a good view of the TV screens. I placed my water bottle in the bottle holder and the monitor on the magazine holder for easy viewing and started it in display and record mode. I placed my ear buds in my ears and plugged into the TV receiver jack. I started pumping the machine to activate it. As soon as the display came to life, I applied the secret keyboard sequence to enter the owner's programming mode. I did not want to be interrupted every twenty minutes by the time limit imposed by the center, forcing me to reset the machine and start over. The manufacturer had a default max of one hour. I could cope with one reset for the entire workout of two hours.

I must repeat my warning to the reader. At this point, I was in excellent physical condition and had been running distance races on a regular basis. I was confident that my diet had restored the endothelial lining of my coronary arteries to a state where they would respond with angiogenesis when placed under extreme stress. I venture to say that anyone with diseased coronary arteries who follows the procedure I am about to describe would probably experience a heart attack and possible death.

I started my warm-up on the elliptical trainer gradually by increasing both resistance level and speed over a ten-minute period to a resistance level setting of fifteen. The range on this particular model is level one to twenty on the resistance setting. From this point forward, I would use the speed of my arms and legs to modulate the work load on my heart and carefully monitor the ST segment of my ECG. I was now working very hard and had worked up a sweat. I started to very slowly increase my speed until I could see a noticeable depression in the ST segment of my ECG indicating left ventricle heart ischemia. At this point, I added just a little more speed and held that speed until the machine timed out at one hour. I did a quick reset, put the resistance back to level fifteen and resumed pumping my arms and legs at the same speed, only removing my arm from the machine arm to take water from time to time. When the elliptical timed out on the second hour, I backed the resistance down to ten for one minute, and then eight for the next minute, and then two for a five-minute cool down, pumping my arms and legs at a walking speed. I then applied the "secret key sequence" to restore the elliptical to the center's twenty-minute time limit. I climbed off, walked over to pick up some cleaning solution and a handful of paper towels, and cleaned up the sweaty mess I had left all over the machine and the floor. At this point, I was a *hungry camper*. I drove home, picked up my wife, Barbara, and drove to my favorite Vietnamese restaurant for a big bowl of *Pho* vegetable soup.

I had planned on following this procedure every day for two weeks but skipped a couple of days to work on my strength training and was too fatigued to do the full two hours on those days. As I proceeded to approach the two-week mark, it became harder and harder to depress the ST segment of my ECG. As planned, after two weeks, I switched over to the interval protocol I had developed. It would stress my heart in intervals, and I could complete my daily workout in forty minutes. I follow this daily routine to this day with the only exception on days I participate in a distance trail race or days that Barbara and I do a long bike ride. We ride anywhere from twelve to sixty miles, depending on weather and time constraints. When I bike, I try to do some interval work by riding at about twenty miles per hour for a short distance and then waiting for Barbara to catch up to me and continue at about a twelve– to fifteenmile-per-hour pace.

MY DAILY INTERVAL EXERCISE PROTOCOL

FOR STARTERS, ONE MUST PURCHASE A HEART rate monitor. They are readily available at sporting goods, running, or biking stores. A decent one can be purchased for less than $100. Some have complex features, but the only essential feature is heart rate. I have been using the same Polar monitor I purchased in 1993, following my first heart surgery. Next, one must calculate their maximum age-adjusted heart rate. As a general rule, 220 minus one's age will get you a ballpark max heart rate. One must then calculate two numbers and remember them. First, we need to remember 70 percent of our maximum rate, and second, 90 percent of ours maximum heart rate. The choice of exercise is yours, depending on many personal factors. You can use this protocol while running, biking, swimming, or on your favorite exercise machine. I strength train with weights three days a week and plan for a daily cardiovascular workout everyday with an occasional rest day usually once a week. My favorite machine is the elliptical equipped with arms, since they are easy on the joints. To avoid injury, I recommend cross training and not adding more than 10 percent a week to workload, speed, or distance. Avoid exercises that twist or place torsional forces on the joints. As I tell the ladies in our aerobics class "you need to stress your skeletal system to maintain bone density by lifting weights or doing some impact exercise." I usually stress the point that it is more important for the ladies to lift weight than men, since they are more prone to osteoporosis.

I will now describe a typical session on the elliptical trainer. I use the quick start mode on the machine, placing it in manual mode. You don't want the machine program driving your workout. Depending on the exercise machine and model, you may have to select manual mode. I also set the timer mode to ascending since many of the machines descend time from start time. I start the warm-up phase by increasing both resistance and speed over a ten-minute period to achieve my 70 percent of maximum age-adjusted heart rate. Most machines have a one to twenty resistance level. As I complete the ten-minute warm-up phase, my resistance level is set to ten. Next, I set the resistance level to fifteen and increase my speed to achieve an age adjusted heart rate of 90 percent of max. I hold this level for a four-minute interval until the total time reaches fourteen minutes. Now, I take the level back to ten for a three-minute interval until the total time reaches seventeen minutes. Now, I go back to level fifteen until the total time reaches twenty-one minutes. Then, I go back to level ten until total time reaches twenty-four minutes. Then, I increase the level to fifteen until total time reaches twenty-eight minutes. Then, I put the level down to ten until total time reaches thirty-one minutes. Then, I go back to level fifteen until total time reaches thirty-five minutes. At this point, we have achieved our goal of four intervals at 90 percent with a duration of four minutes separated by four intervals of 70 percent with a duration of three minutes. Now, I can slow down and put back the resistance level down to level eight and then down to level two at forty minutes total time for a five-minute cool down. I am done and will need the cleaning solution and paper towels to clean up the machine for the next customer. I wear my heart monitor strap and wristwatch to monitor heart rate. Some machines will help by displaying heart rate on the machine display.

ITS TIME FOR MORE HEART IMAGES

KETTERING HOSPITAL IS ABOUT TWO MILES FROM my home where some friends of mine work. I was told that the hospital was planning on installing a 64 slice CT scanner. I did some detective work and acquired the name of the 3D imaging specialist at the hospital. I found him at the hospital and told him I wanted to volunteer as a test subject and shared my story with him. Tom put me in touch with the then head of radiology, and I was once again in the *volunteer business*. I signed the necessary release and was scanned shortly after the installation of the scanner. A couple of days later, Tom invited me into his 3D lab, and we viewed the images together. I had asked him to pay special attention to two areas. First, I wanted to know if he had found any calcium on my donated aortic valve. There was none. Next, we were looking for signs of coronary arterial growth. Tom was very excited and showed me a 3D color image of an artery grown around the apex of my heart connecting my LAD (left anterior descending) to my PDA (posterior descending artery) and was feeding it blood in what he called "retrograde" (backward). The animal researchers were right on! When healthy ischemic tissue is stressed it responds with angiogenesis regardless of the living organism. As we will see later in this story, I would get the opportunity to thank them in a very special way.

IT WAS TIME TO PROVE TO THE FAA I NO LONGER HAD ISCHEMIA

FROM ALL MY DEALINGS, STARTING AS A novice in 2006 with the FAA, I had learned that they had *their* way of doing things and would only accept information in a format they, as a government agency, would dictate. I had tried using so-called *industry experts* to fight this battle to no avail. At one point, I even enlisted my congressman who tried to take my fight through the Department of Transportation. They just referred back to the FAA. Now my cardiology research would pay dividends. I had a huge mountain to climb, convincing the FAA to issue me a medical certificate. Both coronary artery disease or valve replacements are disqualifying conditions. I would have to follow two guidelines designed for AMEs (Airman Medical Examiners). My only course would be to convince them to issue what they call a "special issuance." Armed with my cardiology knowledge, I would have to do this myself. To appreciate my task, I will list the AME guidelines in the Appendix at the end of the story. Anyone with heart disease desiring an airmen's medical should read these recommendations carefully and take charge of the results submitted to the FAA.

The last guideline in the appendix is the stress test requirement. I felt this was the key to convincing the cardiology contractor they would surely refer me. I was determined *not* to allow my cardiologist to supply any information this time, since in the past, his staff had just dumped my entire file on them. I had learned never supply more than what they ask for. If you bury them in paper, they will bury you. They already had a mountain of records in my file.

I put together a plan. Instead of just mailing my request to the FAA bureaucracy in Oklahoma City as I have done in the past, I would first contact the Great Lakes Region flight surgeon responsible for my area. I called him and told my story. I then requested his assistance in supplying a *heads up* to their cardiologist in Oklahoma City. I could then direct my request for a *special issue* medical certificate directly to his attention. He liked my story and agreed to contact the cardiologist and have him expect a letter from me.

I was due for a stress test with my cardiologist and called his office prior to my annual exam and requested the stress test. It was scheduled for the morning of March 13, 2012. I took charge of this stress test myself. I would not allow anything to go wrong. I arrived wearing my running shorts, tank top, and lightweight road shoes. I was prepared to run. The total procedure will take all morning since they require two scans to acquire rest and stress images. The staged run is performed according to the Bruce Protocol, a stress test on a treadmill that increases the percent of grade as well as the speed of the treadmill every three minutes. They also require the patient to eat a meal before the last scan as well as drink a lot of water to flush out the radioactive isotope they inject at maximum stress on the treadmill.

When my time came to run, I removed my shirt and had the EKG electrodes attached to my chest. One of the nurses then stuck an IV in my arm to allow them to inject the radioactive isotope when I yelled "enough." The treadmill is completely computer controlled and displays a live EKG trace, percentage of maximum heart rate, time, speed, level, stage etc. The nurse must manually work the blood pressure cuff and inject the isotope at the proper time. They told me they would inject me when I achieved 90 percent of my maximum heart rate on the display. I replied, "No, I will tell you when to inject after I exceed 100 percent of my maximum heart rate." I was determined to prove I no longer had ischemia to the FAA.

I ran as if I were running a race with a sprint to the finish. It starts out at a slow walk and ends in a dead run uphill. I closely monitored the display, and when my heart rate was clearly well over 100 percent, I yelled at the anxious staff to inject me with the radioactive isotope. There would be no cool down today. They just stopped the treadmill and had me sit down while they monitored recovery blood pressure and EKG. I ate and then drank more water before lying on the scanner table for about twenty minutes and finished the final scan.

My follow-up appointment was scheduled with my cardiologist a week later. We then reviewed the results. I obtained my copy of the results from the hospital ahead of time and reviewed it myself. This is what I had been waiting for so many years: *There was no evidence of stress-induced ischemia* by either ECG criteria or scintigraphic evidence. My stress images were actually better than my rest images even though I had pushed my heart beyond 100 percent. As Dr. Esselstyn said, "I was both heart attack and stroke proof." I think I finally made my cardiologist a *believer*. He said to me, "John, I'm not sure I understand what you are doing, just keep doing it!"

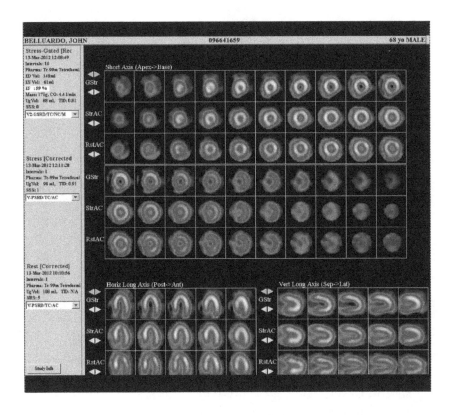

NO ISCHEMIA

I WAS NOW ARMED WITH THE PROOF needed to convince the FAA that I had reversed my heart disease! I copied the complete report along with a CD of my images, put a one paragraph cover letter on top, and mailed the package to the attention of the FAA cardiologist at the FAA Aerospace Medical Certification Division in Oklahoma City. They replied about three months later on the twenty-seventh of June. For the first time ever, it also contained the letter written to them by the cardiology consultant. He recommended me for approval but wanted one additional test done, a twenty-four-hour Holter monitor test as well as a fresh AME physical exam with up-to-date blood work. I was almost tempted to use my own Holter monitor but decided it would look better coming from my cardiologist. I called his office and spoke to his nurse, Debbie (we were now friends on a first-name basis), and she made the arrangements for me to stop by and wear the monitor for twenty-four hours, returning it the following day.

I returned a couple of days later and picked up the results along with my latest blood test report. I still needed a fresh AME physical exam and contacted Doc Terrell in Hillsboro, Ohio, who had performed most of my physical exams in the past. He was getting ready to retire and had tried many times to get the FAA to issue me a medical. I thought it would be appropriate to let him submit the final physical exam that would result in a medical certificate. I made an appointment and with the Holter report and a fresh blood test report in hand, flew Buster over to Highland County Airport, jumped into the old beat-up ex-police cruiser airport car, and drove over to Doc's house for the physical exam. It was good to see old Doc again. We filled out all the FAA forms. He gave me a thorough physical exam and made sure I could still see without color blindness. He would do the *one-package mailing* to the FAA. A few months later, Barbara and I flew over to Highland County Airport on a very windy day and celebrated Doc's retirement party in a hangar there.

THE BATTLE IS WON!

ON SEPTEMBER 21, THE FAA ISSUED ME a third class medical certificate. Finally, my almost seven-year battle had been won! There were still some issues to contend with. I was still carrying both a student pilot certificate and a pilot certificate issued by John Lane who was now deceased. None of the local CFIs were sure of my status or what I should do next. I went all the way up the chain of FAA bureaucracy to Oklahoma City, and they finally came to the conclusion that my pilot certificate issued by John Lane was invalid, but the student pilot certificate he had issued me was still valid after all these years. Unfortunately, my written pilot test had run out after two years, and I would have to take another as well as another check ride. I took another written test at Moraine Airpark where I had taken the previous one and passed with no problem. Now, all I needed was another check ride. I could pay a designated pilot examiner (DPE) for a check ride or get a free one from the FAA. I thought to myself, "I paid for the first one. I'll get a free one from the FAA." I called the Cincinnati FSDO, requesting a check ride and was told they had no one on their staff qualified to fly a Luscombe.

How interesting. I could probably teach them how to fly a Luscombe! I took my original check ride with flying legend John Lane and asked another, Martha Lunken. I thought to myself, "She won't be afraid to fly a Luscombe." I went up with Martha. Not only is she a very skilled pilot, but also a dear lady as well. I did all the necessary pilot maneuvers, and we had some fun doing steep turns with Buster. She admired the responsiveness of the Luscombe. Unlike my check ride with John Lane, she did not require a spin. Though Martha pushed me close to spin entry with a stall. It was October ninth, a few weeks later my permanent plastic pilot's certificate arrived in the mail.

John completes his *check ride* with Martha Lunken.

THE NEW YORK FIFTIETH
CLASS REUNION

I MUST JUMP BACK A COUPLE OF years momentarily. Miriam, one of my high school classmates had been planning our fiftieth class reunion for many years, starting all the way back at the time of our fortieth reunion. Barbara and I had attended the fortieth back in Long Island where we grew up. Miriam, being the *ultimate* event organizer, constantly stayed in touch with everyone, planning for this to be *a big event*. Barbara and I had blocked our calendar and planned to spend time with my cousin, Terry, and her husband, Art, in New Jersey. We reserved a motel room in Long Island for the weekend activities associated with the reunion. By that time, I had already flown the Luscombe to New York City twice and now planning my third trip.

It was mid-October 2011, and I paid special interest to the long-range weather forecast, noting that the normal west winds aloft were unusually strong that fall. I normally fly as low as I can with head winds and as high as I can with a tail wind. Buster cruises at an air speed of 87 kt. (100 mph). My two previous trips to the New York area took anywhere from five to six hours total with a gas/lunch stop about halfway in Pennsylvania. We took off from Red Stewart Field on the morning of the 17th, and as I started to climb, we experienced a dramatic increase in ground speed. I decided to get as much tail wind as possible and went to 10,000 ft. We were in a 70-kt. tail wind and our little 65hp Luscombe was booking along at 180 mph ground speed! To this day, that is the fastest trip I have ever made. We went from Waynesville, Ohio, to Morristown, New Jersey, in a little over two and a half hours in a Luscombe!

We tied Buster down at Morristown, and my cousin drove us to their home in Park Ridge. We would spend the remainder of the week with them. Terry and Art, as lifelong New York area residents, had never visited The Statue of Liberty or Ellis Island. Barbara and I had visited both a number of times on return trips to New York. Both landmarks have always held a special meaning for me. All four of my grandparents entered this country through the *Great Hall* of Ellis Island. Our flight down the Hudson River and over the island two years prior had sparked my passion to research their journey to this country. Following that trip, I had uncovered the ship manifests for all of them in the Ellis Island archives. The four of us spent two days visiting both iconic landmarks. That year was also the 125th anniversary of the Statue of Liberty. Visiting the island can be a very moving experience for anyone tied to its history. Forty percent of Americans can trace their roots back to at least one ancestor who arrived through Ellis Island.

That Friday morning, I planned on renting a car in New Jersey and driving over to Long Island to our reunion hotel. We awakened to a very windy day in the New York area and reports of a truck having blown over on the George Washington Bridge, causing hours of traffic delays. Having grown up with New York traffic, I decided it would be a lot easier and faster to fly over all the traffic and rent the car in Long Island. Terry and Art dropped us off at Morristown, and we flew over the George Washington Bridge and beat the $13-bridge toll as well, landing at Republic Field in Farmingdale.

Buster getting fueled up at Republic Field in Long Island

AS FATE WOULD HAVE IT

WE SPENT THE WEEKEND REMINISCING WITH OLD classmates at the hotel and a visit to Valley Stream North High School and the reception held in Baldwin. At one point, Barbara and I were seated at the same table with Steve, a classmate I had not seen in fifty years. I started telling him my story of reversing heart disease by growing new arteries in my heart. I went on that I had duplicated the procedures used in animal research studies and had literally used myself as a human guinea pig. He pointed out to us that he was heavily involved in medical research. We immediately hit it off, and he mentioned that he would be chairing an upcoming conference for the Academy of Surgical Research to be held at the end of September 2013. He thought the telling of my story from a patient's perspective at their twenty-ninth annual meeting would be very rewarding for the animal researchers attending. I agreed should he get approval from the Academy. We traded cards and agreed to stay in touch.

The following week, we took off early in the morning from Republic Field, flew north over Long Island Sound to avoid LaGuardia

Airport's class B airspace, used the Tappan Zee Bridge as a way point, and then headed west for home. Unfortunately, the strong winds from the west were still unusually strong. We flew as low as was safe to try and stay out of the head winds. At one point crossing the mountains, we were only making 35 mph ground speed in very turbulent air! After multiple stops for gas, we ran out of daylight near Zanesville, Ohio, and landed for the night. The very nice FBO (Fixed Base Operator) lent us his courtesy van and recommended a nice restaurant and hotel for our overnight stay.

The following morning, we awoke to rain and wind. The rain quit late in the morning, and we finally made it back to Red Stewart Field and home that afternoon, still having fought strong headwinds.

In June 2012, I received an e-mail from Steve with a formal request from the Academy of Surgical Research. They requested a keynote talk from a patient perspective on the benefits of the outcomes of surgical research and new surgical procedures. I had fifteen months to prepare my presentation. I was very excited to share my research since no human research existed. If more of the public could be informed, many lives could be saved.

I created a template based on previous diet-based presentations I had given at a number of public libraries around the state. This one would be different in that I could now include my angiogenesis research based on animal studies. That template has provided me with the outline for this story.

We continued our correspondence over the following months as I adjusted my template to fit the specifics of the very specialized audience I would be making the presentation to. As the time approached, we decided to fly Buster, my Luscombe 8A, to Clearwater Beach for the meeting.

The conference ran from September 26 to 28. We planned to arrive on the twenty-sixth and depart the morning of the twenty-ninth, allowing for overnight stops in both directions. I normally plan my trips around VFR weather and avoid flying in marginal conditions.

BAD WEATHER

As is usually the case when you must be somewhere on a particular date, the weather does not cooperate! We departed from Waynesville with clear skies and sun in the morning of the twenty-fifth and allowed for two days of flying to reach Clearwater Beach. I had won a gift of fifty gallons of avgas from an airpark in Oneida, Tennessee, and planned to make that our first stop. As soon as we passed the Ohio River, we encountered a cloud ceiling that moved progressively lower as we proceeded south, forcing us to land at Lake Cumberland Regional Airport in Somerset, Kentucky. We waited about an hour and could see daylight above the hills to the south as the ceiling started to lift, allowing us to reach Oneida and top off our wing tanks.

Our next challenge was crossing the mountains to reach the Atlanta area for our overnight stop. As we proceeded south, the ceiling started to drop again. I always have a sectional chart in my lap with my course drawn in red ink, showing alternate airports near the line. The mountains go as high as 7,500 ft., and we were dealing with a low ceiling with no chance of flying over. As I looked for an alternate airport, I flew over the Tennessee River and noticed that it went through the mountains all the way to Chattanooga. There were a number of airports along the river I could divert to if needed. It meandered all over the place and had some switch backs along the way but could get us through the mountains to Chattanooga. The scenery was awesome along both sides of the river, and old Buster had no problem doing steep turns on the switchbacks we encountered. We had five hours of fuel on board and proceeded flying along the river jumping over bridges when we approached a town. The tallest obstacles we encountered were the power lines crossing the river as we passed two power plants located on the banks of the river. We finally made it to downtown Chattanooga where the river made a turn to the north, and the ceiling started to drop too close to the river. We made a quick U-turn and probably scared the hell out of a barge operator.

My next option was Chattanooga Airport just south of downtown. Just as we flew up on the west side of the city, a hole opened up to the south, and we flew up out of the river and headed south toward the east side of Atlanta's class B airspace. We set a course for Covington, Georgia, but once again, the ceiling dropped down below the passes along a line of hills north of the Atlanta area, forcing us to turn back north and proceed west along the hills until we encountered a pass with daylight below the ceiling. We turned south through a pass and crossed the line of hills and landed in Cartersville, Georgia, on the west side of Atlanta's class B airspace. We made Cartersville our dinner and overnight stop.

The next morning, we flew south around and under Atlanta's airspace and then set a course for Cross City, Florida, our planned lunch stop. We flew at about 800 ft. all the way to Cross City over flat country with radio and TV towers as our only obstacles. We were flying over swamp country when we came up on two big crisscross runways that seemed to be in the middle of nowhere. The old timer at the FBO explained that it had been a World War II training field for P-47 pilots. He lent us his beat up x-police cruiser courtesy car and directed us to the charming Cypress Inn *established in 1928*. The town and the restaurant looked like a time capsule from the past.

After lunch, we drove back to the airport under welcome sunny skies. The final leg of our trip took less than an hour and a half with a nice tail wind from the north taking us south along the gulf coast. As we approached Clearwater Beach, I flew down the beach taking pictures and turned west flying over our hotel, The Sand Pearl Resort, overflying the airport and setting up for a *right downwind* for runway 34 into a nice breeze from the north. As it were, the most difficult part of this day's trip was getting over to the hotel. It took some coaxing from the FBO to get Hertz to bring a car to the airport.

Flying over Clearwater Beach, Florida

MY THANK YOU TO THE RESEARCHERS

MY TIME TO SAY THANK YOU HAD finally arrived! I was scheduled that Saturday as the Academy of Surgical Research Luncheon speaker and presented to all attendees of the conference. I followed my outline and *spoke from the heart*, sharing my findings with this group comprised primarily of animal researchers. I had their undivided attention for about forty minutes and related as to how their animal research had inspired me to reverse my heart disease and grow new heart arteries via angiogenesis. Barbara and I packed the Luscombe the following morning for our return trip to Dayton. Now that we had no schedule to follow, the weather cooperated, and we flew to a lunch stop in northern Georgia and then over the mountains at 9,000 ft. for an overnight stay in Knoxville. We cleared the mountains on top of Knoxville's class C controlled airspace that tops out at 5,000 ft. It was kind of fun requesting entry by descending into their controlled airspace from 9,000 ft. on my portable radio. After all, we were flying in a nonelectric Luscombe designed in 1937! They vectored us to a landing at the

Knoxville Downtown Island Airport within sight of downtown. We enjoyed an evening walking the restored market square area, including a great meal at a local vegan restaurant.

Clearing the mountains at 9,000 feet

Climbing up over Knoxville, Tennessee

The next morning, we made a short flight back to Oneida, Tennessee, to top off my wing tanks with the remainder of the fuel I had won from Big South Fork Airpark. We arrived back at Red Stewart Field early Monday afternoon with a big mission accomplished.

LESSONS LEARNED

1. One *must* take complete responsibility for their health. Do your own research and be skeptical of so-called experts peddling books with the latest fad diet. You may have to do some unlearning of old myths we have been taught since childhood. All vegetarians have been asked, "Where do you get your protein?" My favorite reply is another question. "Where does a race horse get his protein?"

2. There is no magic pill to good health. It takes a symphony of plant-based whole food, not any one *super food* to stay healthy.

3. Excess protein in the diet can be damaging to health and longevity. We should only consume enough protein to meet the needs of our activity level.

4. Animal products, including dairy, should be avoided. We have all been indoctrinated by both government and the

dairy industry that we need milk products to avoid osteoporosis when just the opposite is true. Dairy products tend to add to blood acidity, making it easy for the body to leach calcium from the bones when needed. Green leafy vegetables like Kale and collard greens should be our primary source of calcium. You cannot eat too many green leafy vegetables. Your mother was right when she told you to "eat your spinach!" On this topic, I will leave the reader with a thought-provoking question. Name any animal on the face of the earth that continues to drink milk after it is weaned? If you want to look like a calf you should drink cow's milk!

5. Do not add liquid oil to your diet including the so-called *good oils*. They just add unnecessary calories to your diet and contribute to inflammation of the endothelial lining of the arteries. Almost everything you eat contain natural oils. If you are concerned about getting enough omega 3 oil in your diet, take a couple of tablespoons of ground flax seed with breakfast.

6. Processed food should be avoided. If it sits on the supermarket shelf for three months and does not get moldy, you do not want to eat it! On this subject I must add that we should avoid pesticides and genetically modified foods by eating organically grown fruits, vegetables and grains. Our government regulators are being influenced by agribusiness and chemical companies obsessed with engineering the pesticides into our food supply. If it kills the insects and prevents the bee population from reproducing it will likewise do the same to us.

7. Avoid processed grains. No white rice. No white bread. They have a high glycemic index and can contribute to diabetes. If it grew on a farm, eat it. If it grew in a factory, avoid it!

8. Avoid restaurant food unless you make friends with the chef. Most restaurant food has too much salt, fat, and sugar. All three cause inflammation in your body. Barbara and I eat

out often, and we have made friends with the chef and rarely order anything from the menu.

9. Be careful with nutritional advice from so-called experts. Some doctors study nutrition, but most get very little training in this subject. Ask where their nutritional expertise was acquired. Far too many doctors are treating symptoms and not the cause of a condition. If you need proof, just look at the number of stent procedures and heart bypass surgeries performed in this country. Neither of these addresses the root cause of heart disease. Be wary of overly prescribed medications. Many are influenced by the pharmaceutical industry that tends to peddle free samples to the medical community. The drug companies can't make a living telling you to follow a healthy lifestyle.

10. If you don't use it, you will lose it. One must make a commitment to regular exercise to maintain fitness. Cardiovascular exercise should be a daily activity and strength training should be done at least three days a week. The cardiovascular system should be stressed with interval training as outlined in my story. While on the subject of exercise, don't forget *that food trumps everything*, including genetics and exercise. As I mentioned earlier in this story and deserves repeating, "All my first cousins died of heart disease in their early sixties." They consumed the typical *western diet* and died prematurely from it.

The choice is yours. You can make yourself both "heart attack and stroke proof" as Dr. Esselstyn would say or continue to eat the western diet into sickness and a shortened life. As the old cliché goes, "You are what you eat." Please don't be a fatalist. I have heard too many times "you have to die sometime, and I am going to eat what I want." When I hear this, I would like to respond with "go ahead and eat what you want and spend the last twenty years of your life in a nursing home being a burden to your children." I've never used it but can't count the number of times that response has been on the tip of my tongue. I will close where I started: "Never, never, never give up."

APPENDIX

Guide for Aviation Medical Examiners

Decision Considerations
Disease Protocols—Coronary Heart Disease

A. Requirements are for consideration for any class of airman medical certification.

    1.   Recovery periods before consideration can be given for medical certification:

        1. 6 months: after angina, infarction, bypass surgery, angioplasty, stenting, rotoblation, or atherectomy

2. 3 months: after ablation or valve repair

3. None: after supraventricular tachycardia, atrial fibrillation, and syncope. NOTE: if any of these conditions required any cardiac intervention that is listed in subparagraphs a and b above, then the applicable waiting periods do apply.

2. Hospital admission summary (history and physical), coronary catheterization report, and operative report regarding all cardiac events and procedures.

3. A current cardiovascular evaluation must include an assessment of personal and family medical history; a clinical cardiac and general physical examination; an assessment and statement regarding the applicant's medications, functional capacity, modifiable cardiovascular risk factors, motivation for any necessary change, prognosis for incapacitation; and blood chemistries (fasting blood sugar and current blood lipid profile to include total cholesterol, HDL, LDL, and triglycerides).

4. A current maximal GXT—See GXT Protocol.

A **SPECT** myocardial perfusion exercise stress test using technetium agents and/or thallium may be required for consideration for any class if clinically indicated or the exercise stress test is abnormal by any of the usual parameters. The interpretive report and all **SPECT** images, preferably in black and white, must be submitted.

Note: If cardiac catheterization and/or coronary angiography have been performed, all reports and the actual films (if films are requested) must be submitted for review. Copies should be made of all films as a safeguard against loss. Films should be labeled with the name of the applicant and a return address.

Guide for Aviation Medical Examine

Decision Considerations
Disease Protocols—Valve Replacement

Applicants with tissue and mechanical valve replacement(s) are considered after the following:

1. A 6-month recovery period shall elapse after the valve replacement to ensure recovery and stabilization. First- and second-class initial applicants are reviewed by the Federal Air Surgeon's cardiology panel;

2. Copies of hospital/medical records pertaining to the valve replacement; include make, model, serial number and size, admission/discharge summaries, operative report, and pathology report;

3. If applicable, a current evaluation from the attending physician regarding the use of Coumadin to confirm stability without complications, drug dose history and schedule, and International Normalized Ratio (INR) values (within acceptable range) accomplished at least **monthly** during the past 6-month period of observation;

4. A current report from the treating physician regarding the status of the cardiac valve replacement. This report should address your general cardiovascular condition, any symptoms of valve or heart failure, any related abnormal physical findings, and must substantiate satisfactory recovery and cardiac function without evidence of embolic phenomena, significant arrhythmia, structural abnormality, or ischemic disease.

5. A current 24-hour Holter monitor evaluation to include select representative tracings;

6. Current M-mode, 2-dimensional echocardiogram with Doppler. Submit the video resulting from this study;

7. A current maximal GXT—See GXT Protocol;

8. If cardiac catheterization and coronary angiography have been performed, all reports and films must be submitted, if requested, for review by the agency. Copies should be made of all films as a safeguard against loss;

9. Following heart valve replacement, first- and second-class certificate holders shall be followed at 6-month intervals with clinical status reports and at 12-month intervals with a CVE, standard ECG, and Doppler echocardiogram. Holter monitoring and GXT's may be required periodically if indicated clinically. For third-class certificate holders, the above followup testing will be required annually unless otherwise indicated.

10. Single, Mechanical and Valvuloplasty—See AASI for Cardiac Valve Replacement;

11. Multiple Heart Valve Replacement. Applicants who have received multiple heart valve replacements must be deferred, however, the AMCD may consider certification of all classes of applicants who have undergone a Ross procedure (pulmonic valve transplanted to the aortic position and pulmonic valve replaced by a bioprosthesis).

It is the responsibility of each applicant to provide the medical information required to determine his/her eligibility for airman medical certification. A medical release form may help in obtaining the necessary information.

All information shall be forwarded in **one mailing** to:

Medical Appeals Section, AAM-313
Aerospace Medical Certification Division
Federal Aviation Administration

Post Office Box 26080
Oklahoma City OK 73125-9914
Medical Appeals Section, AAM-313
Aerospace Medical Certification Division
Federal Aviation Administration
6700 S MacArthur Blvd., Room B-13
Oklahoma City OK 73169

No consideration can be given for Authorization for Special Issuance of a Medical Certificate until all the required data has been received.

Use your full name on any reports or correspondence will aid us in locating your file.

Guide for Aviation Medical Examiners

Decision Considerations
Disease Protocols—Graded Exercise
Stress Test Requirements

An ECG treadmill stress test should achieve 100% of predicted maximal heart rate unless medically contraindicated or prevented either by symptoms or medications. Studies of less than 85% of maximum predicted heart rate and less than 9 minutes of exercise (6 minutes for age 70 or greater) may serve a basis for denial. Beta blockers and calcium channel blockers (spec. diltiazem and verapamil), or digitalis preparations should be discontinued for 48 hours prior to testing (if not contraindicated) in order to obtain maximum heart rate and only with consent of the treating physician.

The worksheet with blood pressure/pulse recordings at various stages, interpretive report, and actual ECG tracings must be submitted. Tracings must include a rhythm strip, a full 12-lead ECG recorded at rest (supine and standing) and during hyperventilation while standing, one or more times during each stage of exercise, at the end of each stage, at peak exercise, and every minute during recovery for at least 5 minutes or until the tracings return to baseline level. Computer generated, sample-cycle ECG tracings are unacceptable in lieu of the standard tracings. If submitted alone, it may result in deferment until this requirement is met.

In patients with bundle branch blocks, LVH, or diffuse ST/T wave changes at rest, it will be necessary to provide a stress echo or nuclear stress test.

Remember a phone call to either AMCD or RFS may avoid unnecessary deferral.

Reasons for not renewing an AASI:

- The applicant is unable to make at least 85% of maximal heart rate on stress testing or less than 9 minutes (6 minutes if age 70 or greater);

- The applicant develops 1 mm or greater ST segment depression at any time during stress testing. Unless the applicant has additional medical evidence such as a nuclear imaging study or a stress echocardiogram showing the absence of reversible ischemia or wall motion abnormalities reviewed and reported by a qualified cardiologist;

- The nuclear stress testing shows evidence of reversible ischemia, a stress echocardiogram shows exercised induced wall motion abnormalities, or either study demonstrates a negative change from the prior study of the same type;

- The ejection fraction on a nuclear stress test or stress echocardiogram is 40% or less; or a 10% decrease from a prior study; or

- The applicant reports any other disqualifying medical condition or undergoes therapy not previously reported.

ABOUT THE AUTHOR

John spent most of his business career with two companies, first with the NCR Corporation where he worked many years in field engineering, sales and product development. A milestone at NCR was working with Paul Allen and Bill Gates, at a then small computer company, in Albuquerque, NM by the name of Altair Computer. (Paul & Bill then started a new company called Microsoft). He then designed the communications extensions to the Basic programming language that were later adopted by both Microsoft and IBM. In 1981, he left NCR and formed his own company (BASS, INC.) where he designed and manufactured the first portable wireless bar code scanning system for the supermarket industry. The company grew very rapidly and provided a comprehensive suite of applications to regional retailers like King Kullen in New York to international retailers like Walmart. At this point in his life he was plagued with heart related health issues and decided to sell his company. He devoted his time to researching heart disease and completing a life style change. He started to run, and has completed many marathons and half marathons. He has had two open heart surgeries, the first in Dayton Ohio in 1993 where he had 5 bypass grafts installed on his heart, and the second at the Cleveland Clinic where 2 more grafts were installed and his bicuspid aortic valve (congenital defect) was replaced with a human donor valve provided by a young man killed in a car wreck.

His extensive research on nutrition and exercise enabled him to state that regardless of genetic predisposition we Americans are dying of the Western diet. His research on human angiogenesis based on animal models is entirely unique and proves that new arteries can be grown in the human heart and completely reverse heart disease.

CPSIA information can be obtained
at www.ICGtesting.com
Printed in the USA
BVHW071916160222
629208BV00002B/200